THE TUTTL ─── and tl

FATE OF THE FUTURE

Books in The Tuttle Twins series:

The Tuttle Twins Learn About the Law
The Tuttle Twins and the Miraculous Pencil
The Tuttle Twins and the Creature from Jekyll Island
The Tuttle Twins and the Food Truck Fiasco
The Tuttle Twins and the Road to Surfdom
The Tuttle Twins and the Golden Rule
The Tuttle Twins and the Search for Atlas
The Tuttle Twins and their Spectacular Show Business
The Tuttle Twins and the Fate of the Future

Find them all at TuttleTwins.com

ISBN 978-1-943521-34-0

Boyack, Connor, author.
Stanfield, Elijah, illustrator.
The Tuttle Twins and the Fate of the Future / Connor Boyack.

Cover design by Elijah Stanfield
Edited and typeset by Connor Boyack

Printed in the United States

10 9 8 7 6 5 4 3

To Lew Rockwell

For spreading Murray's
ideas far and wide.

"The fryer beeped!" Emily exclaimed as she and the other children rushed into Fred's kitchen.

Mrs. Wakinona set the pan of Mandazi on the counter to cool. Ethan's mouth began to water as he watched her sprinkle sugar on top.

"This looks just like the picture in the book we read about Uganda!" Aaron said as his mother smiled widely. "That's right," she replied. "This treat is very popular in my family's culture. I'm sure you will all love it!"

Ethan, Emily, and many other children from the neighborhood loved participating in Fred's book club. Each family took a turn choosing a theme for the month and organizing an activity to help them share what they all learned in the books they chose.

Aaron wanted to share about Uganda, a country in Africa where his mom grew up—and so he chose "People of the World" as his theme. Making and eating Mandazi together was the activity.

The other children had read about different countries. They all wore traditional clothing of the cultures they had learned about.

"I hope you and your sister pick a theme that also has yummy food," Mr. Tuttle told Ethan between bites. "This stuff is so good!"

It was the twins' turn to pick the next theme, but they weren't quite sure what to choose yet.

That evening the Tuttle family had a movie night. Mr. Tuttle decided they would watch a *dystopian* movie—a story that describes an awful future where powerful people usually control others.

The movie showed a world of poor people forced to work in jobs they were given by those in power. Anybody who fought back was taken by robots and sent to work on an asteroid as space slaves. Some rebels fought back and won, setting everybody free—but the plot still bothered the twins.

"Good thing that was fiction, right?" Mr. Tuttle exhaled in relief as the movie ended.

"I wonder if the future could end up like that?" Emily said nervously. "Everybody was being bossed around by the people who controlled the robots!"

"Dystopian fiction can become reality if we let it," Mrs. Tuttle replied as she went to put the ice cream away. "Hey, who ate all the cookies and cream...?"

During a bike ride around their neighborhood the next morning, Mrs. Tuttle noticed the twins yawning repeatedly. "Didn't sleep well?" she asked.

Ethan admitted that he and Emily were so unsettled by the movie that they stayed up for hours talking about the future.

"But we did decide on the theme for the book club," Emily said. "The future—and how we can make it better so all that dystopian stuff never happens."

"Great idea," Mr. Tuttle replied, squirting Emily with his water bottle as she tried to catch him. "What book will you two read?"

The twins didn't know, but they knew someone who could help.

Not surprisingly, they soon found themselves back at Fred's house to get some suggestions; he had an expansive selection in his office. The twins wanted something with a futuristic theme, so Fred led them to a shelf with science fiction and fantasy books.

"I don't want anything dystopian," Emily mentioned. "I need my beauty sleep..."

"And too many kids books just treat us like little babies," Ethan replied. "We want to read something that makes us really think hard about how to make the future better."

"Hmmm..." Fred said, taking a step back to look at his collection. "I definitely have plenty of books that fit that criteria."

Ethan walked to the shelf where Fred kept Bastiat's book, *The Law*, that they had once borrowed.

"How about this one?" Ethan asked, taking a book written by someone named Murray Rothbard. "I've overheard Dad mention this guy before."

"That one will definitely challenge you," Fred laughed. "It might be a little hard to understand, but if you want to avoid a dystopian future, it will definitely help. You two seem up to the task!"

"Anatomy of the State," Emily said, reading the title. "So does it talk about the parts of the body?"

"It must—there's a drawing of somebody's insides on the cover!" Ethan replied. "But what's the state?"

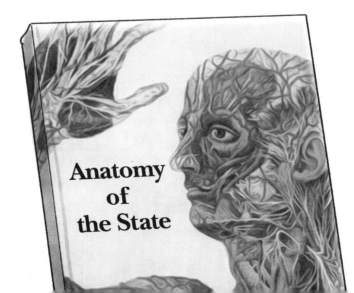

"That's what the book will explain," Fred replied. "Look here." He set a globe in front of them.

"These areas of the world are occupied by different nations—and each is controlled by a state," he said.

The twins noticed how the land was divided up by black lines that cut the globe into different nations.

"But I thought a state is a state—like Texas or New York," Ethan asked. "These are all countries."

"Yes," Fred responded, "but the *state* is also a type of government that controls a certain area on this globe, whether it's a small city or a large nation."

"Remember the theme of our last book club?" Fred asked. "We learned about people all around the world—different *societies*, which are groups of people who live and work together voluntarily."

"Over time, these societies have created cultures—different foods, clothes, music, language, and religions. It's really fascinating to see what people can create when they work together like this."

"That sounds like what Carl talked about at the pencil factory," Emily said, spinning the globe. "People around the world work together to make a simple pencil, even though they are in different... states, I guess you would say."

"That's a great example!" Fred replied. "A state is limited just to the area it controls, but through society we can work together with others, whether it's our neighbors or people around the world."

Fred stopped the globe from spinning by placing his finger on France. "My parents were born here," he said, "and the people—the society—are great! So is the food," he said with a big smile.

Ethan pointed to Scotland. "Here's where some of Dad's family is from."

"And that's where Mom's family comes from," Emily added, pointing to Sweden. She also found the gold star Aaron had placed over Uganda.

"Each of these societies are full of interesting people who work together," Fred explained. "But these nations all have a 'state,' which is a type of government. You'll see how this book talks about the parts of the state—its anatomy—and how that makes it so different from society."

Fred told the twins he would alert the club about their theme for the month, and that he was excited to see what they would learn.

SOCIETY   STATE

Mr. and Mrs. Tuttle were preparing dinner on the backyard patio when the twins returned, holding out the book Fred had let them borrow.

"Fred gave you *Anatomy of the State*?" Mr. Tuttle said in surprise. "This is going to be interesting..."

"He thinks learning about the state will help us avoid dystopian stuff in the future," Emily replied.

"Sounds pretty wise," Mrs. Tuttle replied. "Have you two given any thought to the activity?"

"Not yet," Emily said as she sat down.

Ethan set out the dishes while Emily skimmed the book. There were many passages that Fred had already highlighted.

"Listen to this," Emily said. "It says, 'The state is the systematization of the predatory process over a given territory.'"

"Huh?" Ethan said, looking confused.

"This might not be so easy," Mr. Tuttle smiled as he grabbed his phone. "Let me show you what it means."

Ethan and Emily watched as their dad played a video he found on the Internet of a leopard chasing a gazelle in an African savanna.

The gazelle darted around, trying to escape. But it was no match for the leopard. Mr. Tuttle paused the video as the leopard began eating its new meal.

"That gazelle was the prey," he explained. "So what do we call the leopard?"

"The predator," the twins answered in unison.

ANATOMY OF THE STATE

We are now in a position to answer more fully the question: what is the *State*? The State, in the words of Oppenheimer, is the "organization of the political means"; it is the systematization of the predatory process over a given territory.[4] For crime, at best, is sporadic and uncertain; the parasitism is ephemeral, and the coercive, parasitic lifeline may be cut off at any time by the resistance of the vic-

LIONS / WOLVES

ANATOMY OF THE STATE

We are now in a position to answer more fully the question: what is the *State*? The State, in the words of Oppenheimer, is the "organization of the political means"; it is the systematization of the predatory process over a given territory.[4] For crime, at best, is sporadic and uncertain; the parasitism is ephemeral, and the coercive, parasitic lifeline may be cut off at any time by the resistance of the victims. The State provid...

15

Mr. Tuttle loaded another video after sneaking a few bites of corn.

This one was a story Uncle Ben worked on about rival gangs fighting over an area in their city. Ben interviewed a shop owner who described what it was like living under control of the gang, and how they made him pay money every month—otherwise they would hurt him and destroy his business.

"These gangs want *jurisdiction*—the ability to control what happens in a certain territory," Mr. Tuttle explained. "And they use *coercion*, which means they use violence and threats of violence to get what they want."

"So they're the predators and the shop owner is the prey?" Emily observed.

"Exactly," Mr. Tuttle replied. "But what they are doing is illegal, so the police try to stop them. If you or I tried to bully people in our neighborhood like that, we'd be in a lot of trouble!"

"That brings us to the last point, Emily," Mrs. Tuttle said. "You read about predators in a certain territory becoming part of a system—becoming the normal and accepted way of doing things."

"Most people in charge of the state want to do good things and help people—they're not trying to be bad like gangsters," Mr. Tuttle chimed in. "And many states let the people who live there vote and help decide who should be in charge."

"But even though societies are all different," he continued, "there is one thing about the state that is always the same."

"What's that?" Ethan asked.

"Well, the state always uses coercion against people who might prefer to do something differently than what the state wants," he replied.

"Even if the people in charge are nice, forcing others to do things leads to many problems," Mrs. Tuttle remarked.

COERCIVE GANG

DEMANDS OR ELSE!
1.
2. GIVE

COERCIVE STATE

Taxes or else

ANATOMY OF THE STATE

We are now in a position to answer more fully the question: what is the *State*? The State, in the words of Oppenheimer, is the "organization of the political means"; it is the systematization of the predatory process over a given territory.[4] For crime, at best, is sporadic and uncertain; the parasitism is ephemeral, and the coercive, parasitic lifeline may

"Unfortunately, the problems with the state aren't just in fiction books," Mrs. Tuttle added, setting out the food. "There have been states throughout history... so we can see how they turn out."

She explained how societies want to protect themselves from criminals and invaders, so they form a government and give it power to protect them and defend their lives and their property.

"But that part sounds fine," Emily commented as she scooped baked beans onto her plate. "There are plenty of bad guys in the world."

"That's true," Mr. Tuttle said, "but these governments tend to always expand their power. Instead of just protecting people, they begin controlling them and limiting what they can do."

"The government begins acting less like a protector and more like a predator," Mrs. Tuttle said. "And that's wrong, because we shouldn't be prey."

"That explains why those dystopian stories are so awful," Emily said, thinking of predator bots controlling people.

"It's like the Golden Rule," Ethan said. "Chief Ron said it's never okay to use force in aggression, only in defense. We don't want to be bullied or attacked, so we shouldn't do it to others... and neither should the state!"

"This is also like what we learned about in *The Law*," Emily added. "True laws protect our rights from bad guys, but if the laws are used to control everyone, bad things can happen—and people begin to use the law to boss others around."

"Here's another sentence Fred highlighted," Ethan said, taking the book from Emily. "The history of mankind may be considered as a contest between peaceful cooperation or coercive exploitation."

"That about sums up what we just talked about," Mr. Tuttle replied. "There are two ways to work with others—through coercion, or with *persuasion*, where you convince somebody by explaining something in a way that changes their mind."

Just as the two basic and mutually exclusive interrelations between men are production or predation, so the history of mankind may be considered as a contest between these two principles, peaceful cooperation or coercive exploitation.

"Businesses have to convince people to work for them and to buy their products—they don't force them. And churches and community groups ask for donations and rely on volunteers to help."

Mrs. Tuttle chuckled softly to herself. "Can you imagine a business owner or church leader chasing people down like a predator? We're not gazelles—we're people with rights just like them."

"Yeah, our society wouldn't allow that!" Ethan said.

"You're right." Mr. Tuttle responded. "The people of our city were very upset when they found out that it was Bob the restaurant owner asking the mayor to send the police to shut down the food trucks."

"And with your help informing the public, that food truck fiasco didn't last long," Mrs. Tuttle said proudly. "But here's the big question: if most of us agree that it's wrong to use coercion in society, why do people allow the state to act that way?"

"They're really powerful, so do we even have a choice?" Ethan asked around a mouthful of peas.

"Bob didn't want customers to have a choice. He wanted a monopoly—he wanted to be the only one selling food," Emily added, looking over at Ethan. "And what do monopolies hate?"

"Competition!" Ethan said, snapping his fingers. "I see the problem—every country is run by a single state. It's like there's one big business in charge of making rules for the whole area. People don't really have a choice."

If, then, the State "human family" getting together to decide mutual problems, if it is not a lodge meeting or country club, what is it? Briefly, the State is that organization in society which attempts to maintain a monopoly of the use of force and violence in a given territorial area; in particular, it is the only organization in society that obtains its revenue not by voluntary contribution or payment for services rendered but by coercion.

Mrs. Tuttle smiled, seeing her twins work through the issue. "Here's what Rothbard says about it," she said, opening to another highlighted passage. "The State is that organization in society which attempts to maintain a monopoly of the use of force and violence in a given territorial area."

"It's like Nana said at the ice cream shop," Ethan remembered. "When there's no competition, the business can do a lousy job but still charge everyone a lot of money. Sounds awful!"

"Bingo!" Mr. Tuttle added. "The state never has to rely on persuasion to get what it wants—it has a monopoly no matter what."

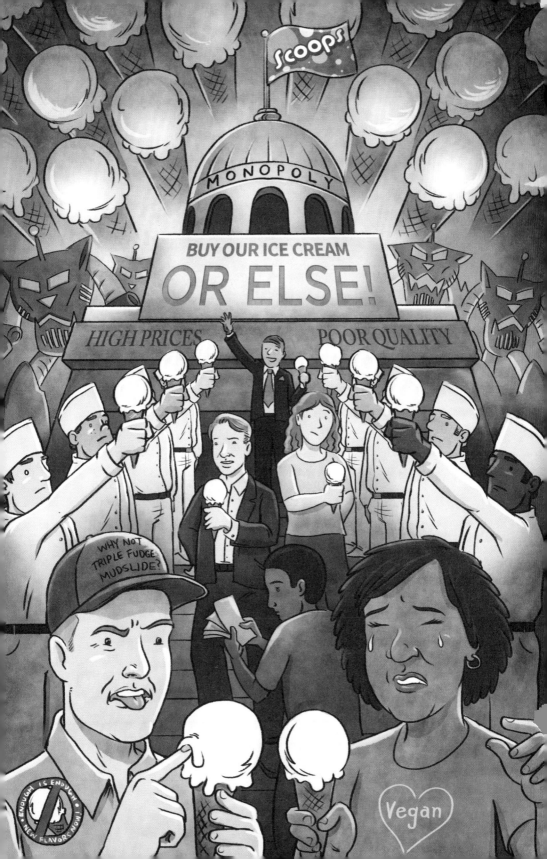

"The state created Surfdom when they took the
Sanchez family's land to build the new road," Ethan
remembered out loud. "Now hardly anyone goes to
La Playa and all the businesses had to close!"

"But guess what?" Emily said, getting a bit riled up.
"There's one business that didn't close: the state. It
caused all of those problems and doesn't have any
competition to challenge it."

Everyone quietly pondered what they had been discussing as they did the dishes together.

"It's important to reflect on stories from the past— even things like the food truck fiasco and the problems with Surfdom," Mrs. Tuttle remarked. "If you care about the fate of the future, history is very important to remember. Answers to our questions can often be found in lessons from the past."

VOLUNTARY GOVERNMENT IN SOCIETY

The twins still hadn't decided on an activity, but continued reading each day as the next book club meeting drew near.

"There's one thing I don't get," Ethan said while playing one evening. "Mr. Rothbard thinks the state isn't good, but there has to be a government, right? Or else, how would society have laws?"

"Actually, a *government* exists whenever a group of people choose rules they agree on," Mr. Tuttle explained. "My company has rules and people in charge—there's a process to 'govern' things. Same with our church and your book club."

"The state is one type of government—but in society there are other types that don't use coercion," Mrs. Tuttle added. "Our family even has a government."

"But we don't get to vote!" Emily remarked, flying a LEGO spaceship toward her dad.

"That's right," Mr. Tuttle added. "Just don't go starting a revolution on us! I don't want any competition for being the boss..."

"I have an idea for the activity," Emily said. "How about we call it 'The Fate of the Future'—each family gets a problem to work on, and they have to come up with ways society can help solve the problem with persuasion instead of coercion."

"And we can build a LEGO society that only uses persuasion!" Ethan said. "It'll be un-dystopian!"

"You mean utopian," Mr. Tuttle smirked. "That's the opposite of dystopian."

WE GET THE BAD GUYS <u>FAST</u> WITH 80% LESS DESTRUCTION

☆☆☆☆☆
HIGHEST RATED JUDGMENTS

"Ethan, you asked if there should be a government," Mrs. Tuttle said. "We do need a set of rules to help protect us from predators."

"But ideally the government would persuade you to do business with them. Rather than bullying people, they would have to be very nice and fair, just like the businesses we shop at every day. They would do their best to serve their customers. They definitely wouldn't tolerate any predators working for them!"

THE BEST VALUE
GUARANTEED!

CUSTOMIZED SECURITY PLANS
FOR YOUR NEEDS

"So the state is okay as long as they have to use persuasion, right?" asked Emily.

"Well, remember," Mr. Tuttle responded, "the state is a monopoly—and so they don't want any competition. Persuasion is important, sure, but it won't really happen unless different governments can compete against each other for your business."

"Society is amazing because there are so many choices," Mrs. Tuttle added. "From the food we eat to the entertainment we watch, we have options— and that makes life interesting and helpful."

"So imagine if there were more choices for the state—for the government we live under," she added. "Wouldn't it be better with more options?"

of all the concepts and institutions that have been tried, none has succeeded in keeping the State in check. The problem of the State is evidently as far from solution as ever. Perhaps new paths of inquiry must be explored, if the successful, final solution of the State question is ever to be attained.

"I'm excited for your activity," Mr. Tuttle said. "And here's why—read the very last thing in the book."

"Perhaps new paths of inquiry must be explored," Emily read, "if the successful, final solution of the State question is ever to be attained."

"Perhaps your group will come up with some creative solutions to how we can live in society without having a state," Mr. Tuttle winked as he sent them upstairs to get ready for bed.

As Ethan thought over what he and his sister had learned, his mind turned to the project and activity. How could a dystopian future be avoided? How do you stop a monopoly? And how do you create a society where people resolve problems without relying on coercion?

It sounded like an awful lot for two nine-year-olds to think about… but after all, they did tell Fred that they wanted to read something that would make them think hard about how to make the future better.

Saturday came quickly, and all the families in the book club arrived at Fred's house eager to talk about the future.

The children gathered around the bins full of LEGO bricks in the living room as the Tuttle twins explained how the activity would work.

"Remember," Ethan announced, "we need to think of how we can avoid a scary future where the state controls us... especially if the people in charge have huge robots that boss everybody around!"

Emily assigned each family a problem to solve without using coercion or relying on the state.

After a bit of time to think it over, Aaron and his mother volunteered to present first.

"Our problem was helping poor people," Aaron said. "We think society can take care of the poor by creating an app that lets people see who in their neighborhood is in need, so they will be more willing to help. Families and friends can use it, too!"

50

"In a dystopian world, taxes are really high," another child said during their turn.

"Our idea is that the state should be like other companies where you pay for what you use. My dad said it's called a 'user fee.' That way, people don't have to pay for things they don't want."

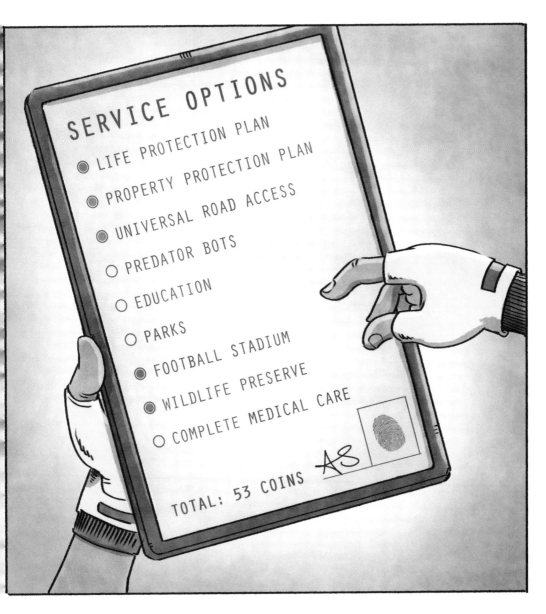

"In a story I read, the government censored important books, controlled the media, and wouldn't let people share their beliefs," another group member said. "But with the Internet, people can share ideas online and get around censorship—so the state can't simply ban books anymore. Our idea is to make a website that lets people share information without being censored or controlled."

"These stories have one state in charge of everyone," Fred said. "So competition is the solution! What if there were different companies you could choose from for protection and justice, no matter where you lived? Then they would compete for your business, trying to keep you happy with low prices and the best services, just like other businesses and organizations do!"

The families began building with LEGO bricks to show their ideas. The twins loved using creative thinking to imagine a better future.

"You know, there's a name for this concept," Fred remarked as Ethan and Emily were hard at work. "It's called *polycentric law*—when two or more governments compete in the same jurisdiction."

"Polycentric law?" Mrs. Tuttle slowly said. "That's a mouthful... but I love the idea!"

The Tuttle twins finished up and began walking around the room to see what each family had done.

The ideas were clever! From the chaos of colored bricks scattered around the room came some fun concepts... and, fortunately, no predator bots!

"When you think about it, the fate of the future really is in your hands," Mr. Tuttle said as the family helped Fred clean up afterward.

"Why do you say that?" Ethan asked.

"Because the future isn't set in stone," Mrs. Tuttle replied. "You get to help change people's minds so they use society instead of the state to get what they want. You can help create a future where people are free to choose for themselves."

"So what do you twins have to say? Since you're in charge of the future, will it have more coercion, or more persuasion?" Fred asked.

"Persuasion, for sure," Emily replied. "That is... unless I'm in charge. Then we'll call it *Emilytopia*!" she declared as she began acting like a predator.

"Not a chance," Ethan said. "*Ethantopia* will be some tough competition for you!"

The End

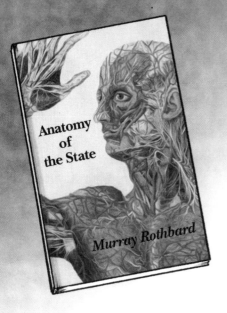

Anatomy
of
the State

Murray Rothbard

"If the bulk of the public were really convinced of the illegitimacy of the State, if it were convinced that the State is nothing more nor less than a bandit gang writ large, then the State would soon collapse to take on no more status or breadth of existence than another mafia gang."

—Murray Rothbard

Born in 1926, Murray Rothbard was an economist, historian, political theorist, and leading thinker in what became the modern libertarian and anarcho-capitalist movements.

Author of over twenty books, he was a consistent champion of personal freedom and free markets, and a reliable critic of harmful government intervention.

His essay *Anatomy of the State* is a short, succinct exposé of how this popular yet predatory system of governance violates our rights, destroys civilization, and ultimately threatens the lives and property of those who are subject to its power.

The Author

Connor Boyack is president of Libertas Institute, a free market think tank in Utah. He is also president of The Association for Teaching Kids Economics, an organization that provides teachers with educational materials and lesson plans to teach economic ideas to their students in a fun and memorable way. Connor is the author of over a dozen books.

A California native and Brigham Young University graduate, Connor currently resides in Lehi, Utah, with his wife and two children.

The Illustrator

Elijah Stanfield is owner of Red House Motion Imaging, a media production company in Washington.

A longtime student of Austrian economics, history, and the classical liberal philosophy, Elijah has dedicated much of his time and energy to promoting the ideas of free markets and individual liberty. Some of his more notable works include producing eight videos in support of Ron Paul's 2012 presidential candidacy. He currently resides in Richland, Washington, with his wife April and their six children.

Contact us at TuttleTwins.com!

Glossary of Terms

Coercion: The use of force or intimidation to obtain compliance.

Dystopia: A society characterized by oppression, misery, and usually significant government coercion over people.

Government: A system of rules to govern the affairs of those within a jurisdiction.

Jurisdiction: The right or authority to exercise control over certain people under certain circumstances or limitations.

Persuasion: Appealing to a person's reason or understanding in order to encourage them to believe or do something.

Polycentric Law: A system of governance in which multiple governments compete or overlap in the same territory.

Society: An organized group of individuals, often who live near one another or have something in common.

State: A form of government that exercises a monopoly of control over people who live in a specific territory.

Discussion Questions

1. Is the existence of the state justified merely because people can vote for who controls it?
2. What are some examples of significant challenges in our society, and how could they be resolved without the state?
3. Why are people often tempted to use coercion to get their way?

Don't Forget the Activity Workbook!

Visit **TuttleTwins.com/FutureWorkbook** to download the PDF and provide your children with all sorts of activities to reinforce the lessons they learned in the book!